Superphonics *Storybooks* will help your child to learn to read using Ruth Miskin's highly effective phonic method. Each story is fun to read and has been carefully written to include particular sounds and spellings.

The Storybooks are graded so your child can progress with confidence from easy words to harder ones. There are four levels - Blue (the easiest), Green, Purple and Turquoise (the hardest). Each level is linked to one of the core *Superphonics* Books.

ISBN: 978 0 340 80547 3

Text copyright © 2002 Gill Munton
Illustrations copyright © 2002 Neal Layton

Editorial by Gill Munton
Design by Sarah Borny

The rights of Gill Munton and Neal Layton to be identified as the author and illustrator of this Work have been asserted by them in accordance with the Copyright, Designs and Patents Act 1988.

First published in Great Britain 2002

10 9 8 7 6 5 4

First published in 2002 by Hodder Children's Books,
a division of Hachette Children's Books,
338 Euston Road, London NW1 3BH
An Hachette UK Company. www.hachette.co.uk

Printed and bound in China by WKT Company Ltd.

A CIP record is registered by and held at the British Library.

Target words

All the Blue Storybooks focus on the following sounds:

a as in **cap** | **e** as in **bed**
i as in **tin** | **o** as in **nod**
u as in **gum** |

These target words are featured in the book:

bad	bed	his	dogfish
can	get	in	got
cap	get(s)	Simsam	Hot Dog
cash	leg(s)	sit	nod
catfish	red	six	posh
fat	them	thin	
fax		this	gum
sad	big	tin	mum
sax	chin	win	pup(s)
tap	did	with	put
that	fish		put(s)
			up

Other words

Also included are some common words (e.g. **play**, **the**) which your child will be learning in his or her first few years at school.

A few other words have been used to help the stories to flow.

Reading the book

1 Make sure you and your child are sitting in a quiet, comfortable place.

2 Tell him or her a little about the stories, without giving too much away:

In the first story, there's a dog who really loves to show off.

In the second story, a little boy is buying a fish in a pet shop. Which one will he choose?

You can join in the game in the last story!

This will give your child a mental picture; having a context for a story makes it easier to read the words.

3 Read the target words (above) together. This will mean that you can both enjoy the stories without having to spend too much time working out the words. Help your child to sound out each word (e.g. **b-i-g**) before saying the whole word.

4 Let your child read each of the stories aloud. Help him or her with any difficult words and discuss the story as you go along. Stop now and again to ask your child to predict what will happen next. This will help you to see whether he or she has understood what has happened so far.

Above all, enjoy the stories, and praise your child's reading!

Ruth Miskin's
Superphonics
Blue Storybook

Hot Dog!

by Gill Munton

Illustrated by Neal Layton

Hodder
Children's
Books

a division of Hachette Children's Books

He's big, bad and red,
With a cap on his head,

Hot Dog!

He likes to play,
he likes to win,
He puts his cash
in a tin,

Hot Dog!

He's got six red pups,
Puts them to bed
(and gets them up),

Hot Dog!

He chews chewing gum
That he gets from his mum,

Hot Dog!

He can play the sax,
He can send you a fax,

Hot Dog!

A thin fish

A fat fish

A dogfish

A catfish

A happy fish

A sad fish

A Mum fish

And a Dad fish

A good fish

A bad fish

A posh fish

A mad fish

A tall fish

A flat fish

 This fish

That fish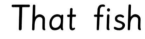

And my fish!

Let's play Simsam Says.

Simsam says:

"Tap your chin."

Simsam says:

"Get up."

Simsam says:

"Sit down."

Simsam says:

"Nod your head."

"Put your legs up."

Did you put
your legs up?